THOMAS MOORE 1779-1852

JOHANNES
BRAHMS
1833-1897

ANTONIN DVORAK
1841-1904

EDVARD GRIEG
1843-1907

FRANZ SCHUBERT
1797-1828

STEPHEN FOSTER
1826-1864

JAMES A. BLAND
1845-1911

The SCRIBNER MUSIC LIBRARY

EDITED BY

ALBERT E. WIER

Volume VIII

Favorite Songs of Every Character

VOCAL

CHARLES SCRIBNER'S SONS, NEW YORK

THE SCRIBNER MUSIC LIBRARY

VOLUME VIII—FAVORITE SONGS OF EVERY CHARACTER

TABLE OF CONTENTS—CLASSIFIED

THE SCRIBNER MUSIC LIBRARY

VOLUME VIII—FAVORITE SONGS OF EVERY CHARACTER

TABLE OF CONTENTS—ALPHABETICAL

A Guide Through Volume VIII

THE volumes of The SCRIBNER MUSIC LIBRARY are devoted entirely to compositions which are heard constantly over the great broadcasting chains—played by orchestras, chamber music organizations or instrumental soloists; sung by choral organizations or by vocal soloists. Each of the volumes contains only the choicest and most popular of its particular type of music.

The compositions in this volume are best described in the exact words of its title—"Favorite Songs of Every Character"—and they are all songs of which we hear at least several daily over the air.

CONCERT SONGS
It would require many volumes to print all the concert songs which are broadcast, therefore it has become necessary to use careful discrimination in the selection of the twenty songs to be found in this volume. Franz Schubert heads the list with his beautiful **Serenade**, his exquisite **Who is Sylvia?** and his cheery **Hark! Hark! the Lark.** There are two songs by Paolo Tosti, the distinguished Italian singing teacher who spent so much of his life in London— **Beauty's Eyes** and **Good-bye**; Johannes Brahms' lovely **Cradle Song** and Jules Massenet's **Elegy** vie in popularity with Tschaikowsky's **Only the Sad of Heart** and Dvořák's **Songs My Mother Taught Me.** Another group of favorites includes Godard's **Florian's Song,** Grieg's **I Love Thee,** the plaintive **Obstination** by Fontenailles, and Lassen's **Thine Eyes So Blue and Tender.** In lighter vein you will find **Fiddle and I,** by Arthur Goodeve; **Love's Old Sweet Song,** by James Molloy; **Non é Ver,** by Tito Mattei; **Mona,** by Stephen Adams; **La Paloma,** by Sebastian Yradier; and the favorite of favorites, **Would God I Were the Tender Apple Blossom,** perhaps known best as the **Londonderry Air.**

FOLK-SONGS
Even more popular with the music audiences are the hundreds of folk-songs which are broadcast as a part of all kinds of programmes, and, in order to discuss those which are included in this volume intelligently, we shall divide them into national groups—mentioning only the most representative. From Wales comes the beautiful **All Through the Night** and the peaceful **Flow Gently, Sweet Afton**; from Hawaii the tender parting song, **Aloha Oe,** its composition attributed to an Hawaiian Queen; from Scotland one of the most exquisite of love songs, **Annie Laurie,** the stirring **Blue Bells of Scotland,** and the wistful **Robin Adair**; from Ireland **Believe Me If All Those Endearing Young Charms** and **Come Back to Erin**; from Italy **Santa Lucia** and **O Sole Mio!** from England **Drink to Me Only with Thine Eyes** and **I'll Sing Thee Songs of Araby**; and in addition, two fascinating coster songs— **The Future Mrs. 'Awkins** and **My Old Dutch**; from Germany the lovely **How Can I Leave Thee!** and Franz Abt's **When the Swallows Homeward Fly.** The above are only a part of the entire group of fifty songs included in this section—each one of them well beloved of the music audiences.

LIGHT-OPERA SONGS
Songs from the light operas are always listened to with appreciation by music lovers, and there is a section devoted to them in this volume. From the Gilbert and Sullivan operas you will find gems such as **The Flowers that Bloom in the Spring** from "The Mikado," **Poor Wand'-ring One** from "The Pirates of Penzance," and **Tit-Willow** from "The Mikado." From

Franz Lehar's world-famous operetta, "The Merry Widow," we have the **Vilia Song** and the languorous **Waltz Song**; from "The Waltz Dream," by Oscar Straus, comes the sprightly **Love's the Tune** and the ravishing **That Viennese Waltz.**   An exquisite ballad, **It Was Not So to Be,** is found in Victor Nessler's "Trumpeter of Sakkingen," and a soothing slumber song in the **Lullaby** from Jakobowski's "Erminie."

HOME SONGS AND PATRIOTIC SONGS
The section devoted to home songs contains several which were enshrined in most of our hearts long before broadcasting was even thought of—that is perhaps why we love to hear them over and over again—for instance, **Auld Lang Syne** with its words by Robert Burns; **Home, Sweet Home,** the words of which came from the pen of an American dramatist, John Howard Payne; and **Grandfather's Clock,** written by Henry C. Work, who also composed many Civil-War songs.   There is also a patriotic section in which will be found all those songs that inspired us in school days, and that still have the power to quicken our pulse whenever we hear them.   It is curious to note that no author or composer has been successful in the conception of an American patriotic song deemed worthy of permanent association with either **America** or **The Star-Spangled Banner.**

SONGS OF THE SOUTH
The songs of our South divide themselves into two classes—minstrel or plantation ditties and the songs of Stephen Foster, the one American balladist whose compositions are known the world over.   In this volume we find his lovely **Come Where My Love Lies Dreaming,** wistful **Jeanie With the Light Brown Hair,** plaintive **Under the Willow She's Sleeping,** and soothing **Beautiful Dreamer.**   Even more famous are **The Old Folks at Home, Hard Times Come Again No More, My Old Kentucky Home,** and **Old Black Joe;** and his keen sense of humor is evident in minstrel effusions which include **De Camptown Races, The Glendy Burke,** and **Ring, Ring de Banjo.**   There are also songs by minstrel singers and composers, such as Dan Emmet's **Dixie Land,** James Stewart's **I Want to See the Old Home,** C. A. White's **I'se 'Gwine Back to Dixie,** and James Bland's **Oh! Dem Golden Slippers!**

COLLEGE SONGS
Despite the fact that the present generation of college youth are presumed to prefer the latest popular songs to the familiar college ditties, we hear the latter frequently broadcast, and the section devoted to them in this volume contains several which are universal favorites.   The list includes **Juanita** and **The Spanish Cavalier,** both songs in Spanish style by American composers; **Dear Evelina, Sweet Evelina** and **Oh, My Darling Clementine; Forsaken** and **Go to Sleep, Lena Darling,** as well as about ten others which bring back happy and sometimes tender recollections to many of us.

Serenade

F. SCHUBERT

Through the leaves the night winds moving   mur - mur low and sweet;

To thy cham-ber window rov - ing Love hath led my   feet.

Si - lent pray'rs of bliss-ful feel - ing Link us though a -

part   Link us though a - part   On the breath of mu - sic steal - ing

To__ thy dream-ing heart,   To__ thy dream-ing heart.

Moonlight on the earth is sleep-ing, Winds are rustling low;

Hark, hark! the Lark

WILLIAM SHAKESPEARE

FR. SCHUBERT

Who is Sylvia?

William Shakespeare

Franz Schubert

Moderato maestoso

1. Who is Syl - via, What is
2. Is she kind, as she is

she___ That all our swains com-mend her?
fair? For beau-ty lives with kind - ness;

Ho - ly fair,___ and wise is she;___ The
To her eyes___ love doth re - pair,___ To

Elegy

English version by
FREDERICK H. MARTENS

J. MASSENET

Fair____ spring of days now gone by,

Once my de-light, You have fore-e'er tak-en flight. And gone is

your a-zure sky. No long-er ring Car-ols of glad birds a-

wing, Voic-ing my joy as they fly! ____ You whom I

love, you have gone _____ as well. Ah,   all too late you re-turn, spring, a-

new! Your sun of   her can-not tell,   Whom I loved true.   Dead are the bright days of

yore! Dark   as the grave is   my heart, and as   cold! Life   joy may

hold _____   Nev - - er - more!

Only The Sad Of Heart

PETER TSCHAIKOWSKY

The vault of
un poco marcato

Heav'n I see Spread far a - bove___ me. Ah! he is

gone, the one who trusts and loves me! On - ly the

sad of heart Can feel my an - guish As from the

Cradle Song

JOHANNES BRAHMS

Con moto *dolce.*

1. Lul - la - by and - good - night! With
2. Lul - la - by and - good - night! With

ro - ses be - dight; Creep in - to thy bed, There pil - low thy
blue eyes close tight; Bright an - gels are near, So sleep with - out

head. If God will thou shalt wake, When the morn - ing doth
fear. They will guard thee from harm, With fair dream - land's sweet

break, If God will thou shalt wake, When the morn - ing doth break.
charm, They will guard thee from harm, With fair dream - land's sweet charm.

I Love Thee
(ICH LIEBE DICH)

EDVARD GRIEG

Light of my life whose i - mage my heart hold - eth!
Du mein Ge - dan - ke, du mein Sein und Wer - den!

Thou at whose feet I wor - ship and ad ore!
Du mei - nes Her - zens er - ste Se - lig - keit!

With wings of love my spi - rit thee en
Ich lie - be dich wie nichts auf die - ser

bliss I set all else be-fore;
Glück ist die - ses Herz geweiht;

wher - ev - er
wie Gott auch

fate my foot-steps may be tak - ing, I love thee dear, I
mag des Le - bens Schick-sal len - ken ich lie - be dich, ich

love thee dear, I love thee dear, now and for - ev - er-more. I
lie - be dich, ich lie - be dich in Zeit und E - wig - keit! Ich

love thee dear, now and for - ev - er-more!
lie - be dich in Zeit und E - wig - keit!

Good-Bye

F. P. TOSTI

swal-lows are mak-ing them read-y to fly, Wheel-ing out on a

wind-y___ sky_____ Good - bye, Summer! Good - bye, good-

bye! Good - bye, Summer! Good - bye, good - - bye!_____

parlato
pp   *molto rall.*

Hush!   A voice from the far - a - way! Listen   and learn,   it seems   to say;   All the to-

poco più   *molto rall.*
col canto

mor-rows shall be as to - day,   All the to - morrows shall   be as to - day. The cord   is frayed, the

rit.   *lentamente*   *cresc. a poco*

cruse   is dry, The link must break,and the lamp must   die_____ Good - bye   to hope! good-

dim.   *col canto*   *cresc.*

bye,   good - bye! Good - bye   to   hope! good - bye,   good   -   bye! _____

rit.

Beauty's Eyes

F.E.WEATHERLY

F. P. TOSTI

I want no stars ___ in Heav'n to guide me, I need no moon, ___ no sun to
I hear no birds ___ at twi-light call - ing, I catch no mu - sic in the

shine ___ While I have you, sweet-heart, ___ be - side me, While I
streams, ___ While your gold - en words are fall - ing, While you

eyes.
own.

p

D.S.

cresc.

dim.

p

D.S.

Piu mosso

Piu mosso

p

I   want no king-dom where thou art, love, I want no throne ____ to make me

p

rit.

olest,   While with - in ____ thy ten-der heart, love, Thou wilt take ____ my heart to

rest.____ King's must play ____ a wea - ry part, love, Thrones must ring with wild a -

larms, But the king - dom of my heart, love, Lies with - in thy lov - ing

arms,____ But the king - dom of my heart, love, Lies with - in thy lov - ing

arms.

Non è ver
('TIS NOT TRUE)

English version by
FREDERICK H. MARTENS

TITO MATTEI

own?

When I vow'd to make thee

mine,

Thou my

love, didst not dis-own! Ah!

no, 'tis not true,

Ah! no,

No, 'tis not true,

no, no!

In Old Madrid

CLIFTON BINGHAM

H. TROTÉRE

1. Long years a - go, in old Mad - rid, Where soft-ly
2. Far, far a - way, from old Mad - rid, Her lov - er

sighs of love the light gui-tar, Two sparkling eyes a lat - tice hid, Two eyes as
fell, long years a - go, for Spain; A con-vent veil those sweet eyes hid, And all the

dark-ly bright as love's own star! There on the case-ment ledge, when day was o'er, A
vows that love had sigh'd were vain! But still, be-tween the dusk and night, 'tis said, Her

ti - ny hand was light - ly laid; A face look'd out, as from the riv - er shore, There
white hand opes the lat - tice wide, The faint sweet ech-o of that ser - e - nade, Floats

stole a ten-der ser - e - nade! Rang the lov - er's hap - py song,
weird-ly o'er the mist-y tide Still she lists her lov - er's song,

Light and low from shore to shore, But, ah! the riv - er flow'd a-long Be -
Still he sings up - on the shore, Tho' flows a stream than all more strong Be -

tween them ev - er - more.
tween them ev - er - more.

Still as the Night

C. BOHM

Florian's Song

English version by
FREDERICK H. MARTENS

B. GODARD

Should in your vil-lage you e'er view ____ him,

A shepherd lad with gen-tle ways; Whose ve-ry sight to love be-

trays, Love that would grow the more you knew him: He is my own,

give him to me! Mine is his heart, ____ my love has he!

And if his voice in ten-der griev - ing,

Sound sweetly thro' your woodlands calm,

And should his plaintive flute hearts

charm, Wake pensive thought with music's weav - ing: He is my own,

give him to me! Mine is his heart, — my love has he!

Obstination

(A Resolve)

H. de FONTENAILLES

It is all in vain to im-
It is all in vain to im-

plore me Not to let her im - age be - guile,
plore me All thoughts of her a - way to keep,

For her face is ev - er be - fore me, And her smile,_____ And her
For still tho' she may ig - nore me, I can weep,_____ I can

a tempo più lento

smile._____
weep._____

It is all in vain to en - treat me

Mem - o - ry's pow-er to de - fy,

For if she wil - leth to de -

feat me, I can die,_____ I can die.

Love's Old Sweet Song.

G. CLIFTON BINGHAM.

J. L. MOLLOY.

22222222222222222

Just a song at twilight, when the lights are low, And the flick-'ring shadows softly come and go, Tho' the heart be weary, sad the day and long, Still to us at twilight comes Love's old song, comes Love's old sweet song.

Vol. VIII-49

Fiddle and I

F.E.WEATHERLY

ARTHUR GOODEVE

By road and riv-er,_____ Coun-try side and town,

I roam for ev-er_____ With my fid-dle brown;_____

Creep-ing un-der barns so glad-ly When out-side the win-ter howls,

51

Andantino
poco tenuto

Down by the wil - low, Sum-mer nights I

lie, _____ Flow'rs for my pil - low, And for roof the

sky; _____ Play - ing all my heart re - mem - bers, Old, old songs from

far a - way; Gold - en Junes and bleak De - cem - bers Rise a - round me

as I play. _____ Ah! it was gay, night and day,

Fair and cloud-y weather, Fid-dle and I, wan-der-ing by,

O-ver the world to-gether, _____ Fid-dle and I, wan-der-ing by,

O-ver the world to-geth - er.

Andantino

On, on for - ev - er, _____ Till the jour - ney ends, _____

Who shall dis - sev - er _____ Us two trust - y friends? _____

a tempo

Who can bring the past be - fore me, Make the fu - ture gai - ly glow,

rit.

Lift the clouds that dark - en o'er me, Like my trust - y fid - - dle

Allegro con spirito

bow? _____ Ah! it was gay, night and day,

Fair and cloud - y weather, _____ Fid-dle and I, wan-der-ing by,

rit. *a tempo*

O-ver the world to - geth-er, _____ Fid-dle and I, wan-der-ing by,

O - ver the world to - geth - - er.

Mona

F.E. WEATHERLY

STEPHEN ADAMS

Songs My Mother Taught Me

ANTON DVOŘÁK, Op. 55, N°4

Now I_ teach my_ chil -

dren each me - lo - dious_ meas - - ure, Oft the

tears_ are_ flow - - ing, oft they flow_____ from my

mem - ry's_ treas - ure.

Thine Eyes so Blue

ED. LASSEN

Very slow with deep feeling

pp

Thine eyes so blue and ten - der,
Thy soft and gold - en tress - es,

When their soft glance I seek, _____ A - wake me to vis - ions of
Like a chain bind my heart _____ So lov - ing and sweet! their ca -

splen - dor, Thoughts that I may not speak. _____ Dear
ress - es Nev - er from me de - part! _____ Ah!

eyes so blue and ten - der, I see them ev - 'ry
bright and silk - en tress - es That haunt me ev - 'ry

Ped. *❋ Ped. simile*

where! _____ My soul like waves __ of o - cean, They
where! _____ As some poor bird __ that flut - ters, My

drown in light __ so fair!
spir - it you__ en -

1.

2.

snare.

a tempo

D.S.

rit.

Ped.

Ped.

Would God I Were the Tender Apple Blossom

(Londonderry Air)

Irish Air

Moderato *Espressivo*

1. Would God I were the ten - der ap - ple blos - som_____ that floats and falls from off the twis - ted bough,_____ To lie and faint with - in your silk - en bos - om, with - in your silk - en bos - - - om, as that does

2. Yea, would to God I were a - mong the ro - ses_____ that lean to kiss you as you flow be - tween,_____ While on the low - est branch a bud un - clos - es, a bud - un_____ clos - - - es, to touch you,

now,_____ Or would I were a lit - tle bur - nish'd
queen,_____ Nay, since you will not love, would I were

ap - ple____ For you to pluck me, glid - ing by so
grow - ing____ A hap - py dai - sy in the gar - den

cold,_____ While sun and shade your robe of lawn will
path,_____ That so your sil - ver foot might press me

dim.

dap - ple,__ Your robe of lawn_ and your hair's_ spun_ gold_____
go - ing,__ Might press me go - ing_ e - ven un - to death!_____

La Paloma
(THE DOVE)

SEBASTIAN YRADIER

The day _____ that I left my home for the roll - ing
And when _____ I come home, from Ni - na to part no

sea, I said _____ "Moth - er dear, oh, pray to thy God for
more, To rest _____ with my moth - er dear on my na - tive

me." _____ And ere _____ we sailed I
shore, _____ A - dieu _____ to the ship

went a fond leave to take _____ Of Ni -
where often with chang - ing mind, _____ I've laughed _____

- na, who wept as if her poor heart would break. "Ni - na, if I should
- and I've wept as veered the light chang - ing wind. Then comes the day, the

die and o'er o-cean's foam _____ Soft - ly a white dove
hap - py and bless - ed day, _____ Chas - ing all sad - ness,

on a fair eve should come. _____ O - pen thy lat - tice, dear-est, for it will
sor-row and care a - way. _____ Ni - na so fair, all smiles will be by my

be _____ My faith-ful soul that lov-ing comes back to thee!" _____
side! _____ Ni - na so dear, will be my own blush-ing bride! _____

Oh! a life on the sea! Sing-ing joy-ous and free, Ah! ___

_____ we're go - ing, None are so gay as we!

Oh! a life on the sea! Sing-ing joy-ous and free, Ah! ___

_____ we're go - ing, None are so gay as we!

All Through the Night

WALTER MAYNARD

1 Sleep, my love, and peace at-tend thee All through the night;
2 Though I roam a min-strel lone-ly, All through the night;

Guard-ian an-gels God will lend thee, All through the night.
My true harp shall praise thee on-ly, All through the night.

Soft, the drow-sy hours are creep-ing, Hill and vale in slum-ber steep-ing,
Love's young dream, a - las! is o - ver, Yet my strains of love shall hov-er,

Love a - lone his watch is keep-ing, All through the night.
Near the pres-ence of my -lov - er, All through the night.

I Would That My Love

H. HEINE

F. MENDELSSOHN

night when thine eye-lids in slum-ber have closed those bright heav'nly beams, Still

there, my love, ___ it will haunt ___ thee, e'en in thy deep-est

dreams, Still there my love, ___ it will haunt thee, e'en in ___ thy deep-est

dreams, e'en in thy deep - est, thy deep-est dreams, ___ E'en ___

in ___ thy deep-est deep - est dreams. ___

The Loreley

F. SILCHER

I'll Sing Thee Songs Of Araby

FREDERIC CLAY

Drink To Me Only With Thine Eyes

Ben Jonson

Old English Air

Slowly

1. Drink to me on-ly with thine eyes, and I will pledge with mine,___
2. I sent thee late a ro-sy wreath,not so much hon-'ring thee,___

Or leave a kiss with-in the cup, and I'll not ask for wine;___ The
As giv-ing it a hope that there it could not with-ered be;___ But

thirst that from the soul doth rise, doth ask a drink di-vine,___
thou there-on did'st on-ly breathe, and send'st it back to me,___

But might I of Jove's nec-tar sip, I would not change for thine.___
Since when it grows and smells, I swear, not of it-self, but thee.___

How Can I Leave Thee!
(True Love)

Folk Song

Lento

1. How can I leave thee! From thee how can I part!
2. Blue is a flow-er-et, Called the "For-get-me-not,"
3. Would I a bird were, Soon at thy side to be!

Robin Adair

Caroline Keppel

Where's all the joy and mirth, Made this town a heav'n on earth?
What when the play was o'er, What made my heart so sore?

Oh! they're all fled, with thee, Rob-in A-dair.
Oh! it was part-ing with Rob-in A-dair.

Ben Bolt

Moderato

Nelson Kneass

1. Oh! don't you re-mem-ber, sweet Al-ice, Ben Bolt, Sweet
2. Oh! don't you re-mem-ber, the wood, Ben Bolt, Near the

Al-ice with hair so brown; She wept with de-light when you
green sun-ny slope of the hill, When oft we have sung 'neath its

gave her a smile, And trem-bled with fear at your frown. In the
wide spread-ing shade, And kept time to the click of the mill. The

old church-yard, in the val-ley, Ben Bolt, In a cor-ner ob-scure and a-
mill has gone to de-cay, Ben Bolt, And a qui-et now reigns all a-

lone _____ They have fit - ted a slab of gran-ite so grey, And sweet
round. _____ See the old rus-tic porch with its ros-es so sweet, Lies

Al - ice lies un - der the stone. They have fit - ted a slab of ___
scat-ter'd and fall'n to the ground. See the old rus-tic porch, with its

gran-ite so grey, And sweet Al- ice lies un - der the stone.
ros - es so sweet, Lies ___ scat-ter'd and fall'n to the ground.

In the Gloaming.

META ORRED

ANNIE F. HARRISON.

Andante.

In the gloam-ing, oh, my dar-ling, when the lights are dim and low;
In the gloam-ing, oh, my dar-ling, think not bit - ter - ly of me;

And the qui - et shad - ows fall - ing, soft - ly come and soft - ly go;
Though I pass'd a - way in si - lence, left you lone - ly, set you free

poco animato — cresc. — rit.

When the winds are sob - bing faint - ly, with a gen - tle un-known woe
For my heart was crushed with long-ing, what had been could nev - er be;

a tempo — dim.

Will you think of me and love me, as you did once long a - go?
It was best to leave you thus, dear, best for you and

best for me. It was best to leave you thus, Best for you and best for me.

Last Night

H. KJERULF

"Alice Where Art Thou?"

W. GURNSEY

J. ASCHER

When the Swallows Homeward Fly

FRANZ ABT

Can ____ I ah! can I e'er know re - pose.

Sally in Our Alley

HENRY CAREY

Andante

Of all the girls ___ that are so smart, ___ There's none like pretty Sal-ly; She is the
Of all the days ___ that's in the week, ___ I dear - ly love but one day, And that's the

dar - ling of my heart, ___ And lives in our ___ al-ley: There is no
day ___ that comes be - twixt, ___ A Sa - tur - day and Monday: O then I'm

la - dy in the land That's half so sweet ___ as ___ Sal - ly; She is the
dress'd all in my best, To walk a - broad ___ with ___ Sal - ly; She is the

dar - ling of my heart, ___ And lives ___ in ___ our ___ al-ley.
dar - ling of my heart, ___ And lives ___ in ___ our ___ al-ley.

Long, Long Ago

T. H. BAYLY

Annie Laurie

LADY JOHN SCOTT

O Blodwen, My True Love

JOSEPH PARRY

Flow Gently, Sweet Afton

ROBERT BURNS

music for - bear, I charge you, dis - turb not the slum-ber-ing fair.
mur-mur-ing stream, Flow gent - ly, sweet Af - ton, dis - turb not her dream.

Comin' Thro' The Rye

ROBERT BURNS

SCOTCH SONG

Gin a bo-dy meet a bo-dy com-in' thro' the rye,
Gin a bo-dy meet a bo-dy com-in' frae the town,
A - mong the train there is a swain I dear - ly lo'e my-sel'

Gin
Gin
But

a ____ bo-dy kiss a bo-dy need a bo - dy cry?
a ____ bo-dy greet a bo-dy need a bo - dy frown?
where's his home and what his name I din - na care to tell!

Ev' - ry las - sie has her lad - die, nane they say, ___ hae I, Yet

a' the lads they smile at me when com - in' through the rye.

Kathleen Mavourneen

MRS. CRAWFORD

F. N. CROUCH

Come Back to Erin

CLARIBEL

hush of the star - ling, O - ver the moun-tain, the Bluffs and the Bays! Then
path o'er the o - cean, Far, far a - way, where my col - leen had flown. Then

Animato

come back to E - rin, Ma - vour - neen, Ma - vour - neen,

Come back a - gain to the land of thy birth,

Come back to E - rin, Ma - vour - neen, Ma - vour - neen,

And it's Kil - lar - ney shall ring with our mirth.

The Kerry Dance

J. L. MOLLOY

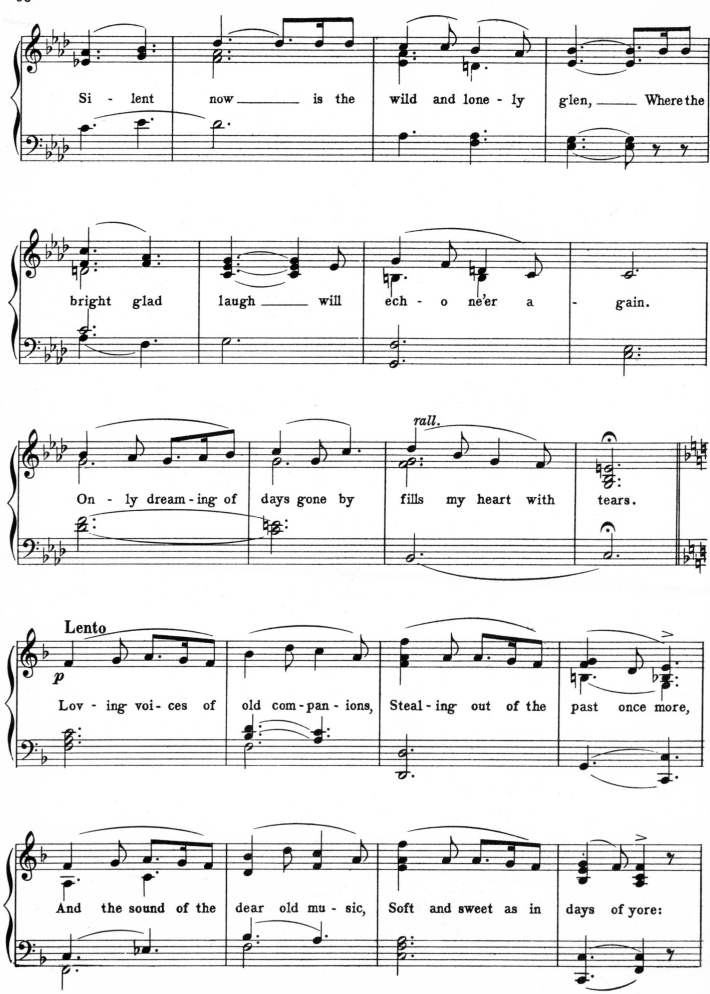

When the boys be - gan to gath - er in the glen, of a sum - mer night,

And the Ker - ry pi - per's tun - ing, Made us long__with wild de - light.

O, to think of it, O, to dream of it, Fills my heart with tears! O, the days of the

Ker - ry danc - ing, O, the ring of the pi - per's tune! O, for one of those

hours of glad - ness, Gone, a - las! like our youth too __ soon! __

The Low Back'd Car

SAMUEL LOVER

Lively but not too fast

1. When first I saw sweet Peg - gy, 'Twas on a mar - ket day: A
2. In bat - tles wide com - mo - tion, The proud and might - y Mars, With

low - back'd car she drove and sat Up - on a truss of hay; But
hos - tile scythes de - mands his tythes Of death, in war - like cars. But

when that hay was bloom - ing grass, And deck'd with flow'rs of spring, No
Peg - gy, peace - ful god - dess, Has darts in her bright eye, That

flow'r was there, that could com - pare, To the bloom - ing girl I sing! As she
knock men down in the mar - ket town, As right and left they fly! While she

sat in her low - back'd car, The man at the turn - pike bar, Nev - er
sits in her low - back'd car, Than bat - tle more dan - g'rous far, For the

ask'd for the toll, But just | rubb'd his auld poll, And look'd | af-ter the low-back'd car.____
doc - tor's art Can-not | cure____ the heart, That is | hit from the low-back'd car.____

The Blue Bells of Scotland

Scotch Folk Song

Moderato

1. Oh! where, tell me where is your High-land lad-die gone? Oh! where, tell me where is your
2. Oh! where, tell me where did your High-land lad-die dwell? Oh! where, tell me where did your

High-land lad-die gone? He's gone with stream-ing ban-ners, Where no-ble deeds are done, And it's
High-land lad-die dwell? He dwelt in bon - nie, Scot-land, Where blooms the sweet blue bell, And it's

oh! in my heart I____ wish him safe at home, He's gone with stream-ing ban-ners, Where
oh! in my heart I____ lo'e my lad-die dwell, He dwelt in bon - nie Scot-land, Where

no - ble deeds are done, And it's | oh! in my heart I____ | wish him safe at home.
blooms the sweet blue bell, And it's | oh! in my heart I____ | lo'e my lad - die dwell.

Believe Me If All Those Endearing Young Charms

THOMAS MOORE

'O Sole Mio!

(My Sun)

E. di CAPUA

1. Be-hold the bril - liant sun in all its splen-dor _ for - got - ten
2. Be-hold the ra - diant sun 'mid eve - ning sha - dows _ with gol - den

is the storm, _ the clouds now va - nish _ The fresh-'ning bree - zes
light it cov - ers all cre - a - tion _ Un - til it sinks be -

heav - y airs will ba - nish _ Be-hold the bril - liant sun in all its
low the world's foun - da - tion _ Be-hold the ra - diant sun 'mid eve - ning

splen - dor! _____ A sun I know of _____ that's bright-er yet, _____
sha - dows! _____

_ This sun, my dear - est _____ 'tis naught but thee _____ Thy

face _____ so fair to see, That _____ shall now my

sun, _____ for - ev - er be! _____ A sun I _

Marie, Mine

HUNGARIAN SONG

Andante

1. Ma - rie, mine, Ma - rie, mine, How thine eyes are danc - ing!
2. Morn-ing's light, Vis-ions bright, But of thee is blend - ing;

Maria, Marì!

ED. DI CAPUA

Carmé

ITALIAN FOLK SONG

Andantino

1. Near the vil - lage there lives a fair mai-den, Who my heart has en - slav'd ev - er
2. From the fields, when her day's work is end - ed, She comes sing - ing a gay, blithe-some

more, And each eve - ning I go to her cot - tage and say as I stand near the
song, And I stand with my heart full of joy As I see her go gay - ly a-

door._____ Sleep, dear Car - mé!_____ for to
long.

sleep is a source of de - light _____ Rest while thy

lov - - - er is guard - ing you all thro' the

night _____ Sleep, dear Car-mé, _____ for to

sleep is a source of de - light _____ Rest while thy

lov- - -er is guard-ing you all thro' the night. _____

Stars of the Summer Night

HENRY W. LONGFELLOW

I. B. WOODBURY

Andante espressivo

1. Stars of the sum-mer night, Far in yon az - ure deeps, Hide, hide your
2. Moon of the sum-mer night, Far down yon west-ern steeps, Sink, sink in

gold-en light, She sleeps, my la-dy sleeps; She sleeps, she sleeps, my la-dy sleeps.
sil - ver light, She sleeps, my la-dy sleeps; She sleeps, she sleeps, my la-dy sleeps.

The Swallow

N. SERRADELL

Where wilt thou go,___ my a - gile lit - tle swal - - low? Thy wings will

tire___ if long thy flight shall be,___ If wind and storm shall bring thee pain and

an - guish, If seek-ing shel - ter none be found for thee ___ A mes - sage

to ___ my lov'd one, wilt thou car - - ry, to tell her

that___ I love her so,___ With joy I'll greet___ thee when thou re-

110

Wot Cher!

(Knocked 'Em in the Old Kent Road)

CHARLES INGLE

Moderato

1. Last week down our al - ley come a toff, Nice old
2. Some says nas - ty things a - bout the moke, One cove

geez - er with a nas - ty cough, Sees my
thinks 'is leg is real - ly broke, That's 'is

Mis - sus, takes 'is top - per off
en - vy, 'cos we're car - riage folk,

In a ve - ry gen - tle - man - ly way! "Ma'am" says
Like the toffs as rides in Rot - ten Row. Straight! it

he, "I 'ave some news to tell, Your rich
woke the al - ley up a bit, Thought our

Un - cle Tom of Cam - ber - well,
lod - ger would 'ave 'ad a fit

cresc.

Popped of re - cent, which it ain't a sell. Leav-ing you 'is lit - tle don - key shay."
When my mis - sus, who's a re - al wit, Says "I 'ates a Bus be-cause it's low!"

Chorus

"Wot cher!" all the neigh-bours cried, Who're yer goin' to meet, Bill? Have yer bought the street, Bill?" Laugh! I thought I should 'ave died Knock'd 'em in the Old Kent Road. Road.

3. When we starts the bless-ed don-key stops,
He won't move, so out I quick-ly lops,
Pals start whack-in' him, when down he drops,
Some-one says he was-n't made to go.
Lor' it might 'ave been a four-in-'and,
My old Dutch knows 'ow to do the grand,
First she bows, and then she waves 'er 'and,
Call-ing out we're go-in' for a blow!

4. Ev'ry eve-nin' on the stroke of five,
Me and Mis-sus takes a lit-tle drive;
You'd say, "Won-der-ful they're still alive"
If you saw that lit-tle don-key go.
I soon showed him that 'e'd have to do,
Just what ev-er he was want-ed to,
Still I shan't for-get that row-dy crew,
'Ol-ler-in' Woa! stea-dy! Ned-dy, Woa!"

Albert Chevalier

My Old Dutch

Charles Ingle

Moderato espressivo

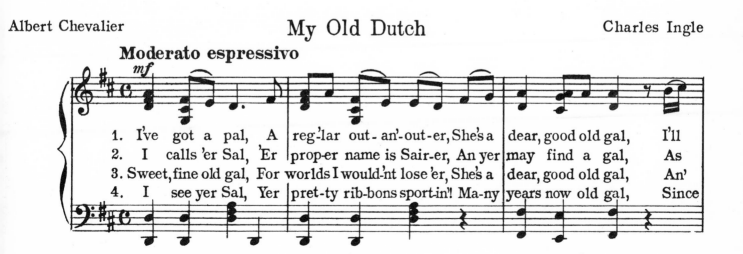

1. I've got a pal, A reg'-lar out-an'-out-er, She's a dear, good old gal, I'll
2. I calls 'er Sal, 'Er prop-er name is Sair-er, An yer may find a gal, As
3. Sweet, fine old gal, For worlds I would-'nt lose 'er, She's a dear, good old gal, An'
4. I see yer Sal, Yer pret-ty rib-bons sport-in'! Ma-ny years now old gal, Since

tell yer all a-bout 'er. It's many years since first we met, 'Er
you'd con-sid-er fair-er; She ain't a an-gel, she can start A
that's what made me choose'er, She's stuck to me thro' thick and thin, When
them young days of court-in'. I ain't a cow-ard, still I trust, When

'air was then as black as jet, It's whit-er now, but she don't fret Not my old gal! We've
jaw-in' till it makes you smart She's just a wo-man bless 'er 'eart, Is my old gal! We've
luck was out, when luck was in; Ah, wot a wife to me she's been, An' wot a pal! We've
we've to part, as part we must, That death may come and take me fust To wait my pal! We've

Chorus

mf a tempo

been to-geth-er now for for-ty years, An' it don't seem a day too much! There

ain't a la-dy liv-in' in the land As I'd swop for my dear, old Dutch There

ain't a la-dy liv-in' in the land As I'd swop for my dear, old Dutch.

The Future Mrs. 'Awkins

ALBERT CHEVALIER

1. I knows a lit-tle do-ner, I'm a-bout to own 'er, She's a-goin' to mar-ry me. At fust she said she would-n't, then she said she could-n't, Then she whis-pered "Well, I'll see." Sez I, "be Mis-sis 'Aw-kins, Mis-sis 'En-'ry 'Aw-kins, Or a-crost the seas I'll roam. So 'elp me bob I'm cra-zy, Li-zer you're a dai-zy, Won't yer share my 'um-ble

2. I shan't for-git our meet-in' "G'-arm," was 'er greet-in,' "Just yer mind wot you're a-bout; 'Er pret-ty 'ead she throws up, then she turns 'er nose up, Say-in' "let me go, I'll shout! "I like your style,'sez Li-zer, thought as I'd sur-prise 'er, Cops 'er round the waist like this! Sez she "I must be dream-in,' Chuck it I'll start scream-in,'" "If yer do" sez I, "I'll

3. She wears a art-ful bon-net, fea-thers stuck up-on it, Cov-er-in' a fringe all curled; She's just a-bout the sweet-est, pret ti-est and neat-est Do-ner in the wide, wide world! And she'll be Mis-sis 'Aw-kins, Mis-sis 'En-'ry 'Aw-kins Got 'er for to name the day; Set-tled it last Mon-day so to church on Sun-day Off we trots the don-key

cresc.

"'ome?" "Won't yer?" Oh! Li - zer! Sweet Li - zer!
kiss." "Now then" Oh! Li - zer! Sweet Li - zer!
shay! "Now then" Oh! Li - zer! Sweet Li - zer!

If yer die an old maid you'll 'ave on - ly yer-self to blame! D'y'ear Li - zer?
If yer die an old maid you'll 'ave on - ly yer-self to blame! D'y'ear Li - zer?
If yer die an old maid you'll 'ave on - ly yer-self to blame! D'y'ear Li - zer?

Dear Li - zer! 'Ow d'yer fan - cy 'Aw-kins for yer o - ther name?
Dear Li - zer! 'Ow d'yer fan - cy 'Aw-kins for yer o - ther name?
Dear Li - zer! Mis - sis 'En' - ry 'Aw-kins is a fust class name?

Darling Nelly Gray

B. R. Hanby

Moderato

1. There's a low — green — val - ley on the old Ken-tuck-y shore, There I've
2. One — night I went to see her, but "she's gone!" the neighbors say, The —
3. My — eyes are get-ting blind-ed, and I can not see the way, Hark! there's

whiled many hap-py hours a - way, A - sit-ting and a-sing-ing by the
white man bound her with his chain, They have tak-en her to Georgia for to
some - bo-dy knock-ing at the door, Oh! I hear the an-gels call-ing and I

When the Corn is Waving, Annie Dear

C. Blamphin

Moderato

1. When the corn is wav-ing An-nie dear, Oh meet me by the stile, To
2. When the corn is wav-ing An-nie dear, Our tales of love we'll tell, Be-

hear thy gen-tle voice a-gain, And greet thy win-ning smile; The
side the gen-tle flow-ing stream, That both our hearts know well; Where

moon will be at full, love, The stars will bright-ly gleam, Oh, come, my Queen of
wild flow'rs in their beau-ty, Will scent the ev-'ning breeze, Oh, haste, the stars are

night, love, And grace the beauteous scene When the corn is wav-ing, An-nie dear, Oh,
peep-ing, And the moon's be-hind the trees,

meet me by the stile, To hear thy gen-tle voice a-gain, And greet thy winning smile.

Aloha Oe

HAWAIIAN FOLK SONG

Moderato espressivo

1. Now has come the hour sad of part-ing, Our
2. When you're far a-way, ah! think of me, love, As

day-dream of love, my own, is o'er, On-ly mem-o-ries will soon be
I will be dream-ing e'er of you, Let fond rec-ol-lec-tion be your

left us, As our lives seem to glide on as be-fore! Fare-
fan-cy, And to me may your heart be ev-er true!

CHORUS

well, dear love, I'll dream of you, No pass-ing grief is this my heart is feel-ing, I

love you so, be-fore you go, I'll say "Dear lov'd one, fare-well!"

Love Thoughts

HAWAIIAN FOLK SONG

I think of you, when the mists are fall - ing, And all the world has gone to seek sweet rest Oh! the long-ing in my heart is

ev - er, ev - er grow - ing, All that I ask of you is love.

REFRAIN (Harp effect)

There on the heights, mists are soft - ly fall - ing, Here in my

heart fierce long-ing fills my fond soul An-swer, love, that you are mine, that

noth-ing e'er shall part us, That you are mine, mine a - lone.

Santa Lucia

NEAPOLITAN SONG

Moderato

Calm o'er the o - cean blue Moon - light is shin - ing
While from the blue ex - panse Fair stars are gleam - ing

And with its sil - ver light Stray cloud is lin - ing,
O - ver the night be - neath, In sweet - ness beam - ing.

Come pret - ty mai - den, look from thy lat - tice, love,
As o'er the stream we glide, borne by the roll - ing tide.

List to the boat - men Chant - ing and row - ing.
* San - ta Lu - ci - a, San - ta Lu - ci - a.

* Pronounced Lu-ché-a

Bonny Eloise

J. R. Thomas

Wait For The Wagon

R. B. Buckley

Sweet Genevieve

Henry Tucker

still the hands of mem-'ry weave, The bliss-ful dreams of long a-go.

The Girl I Left Behind Me

Samuel Lover

1. The hour was sad I left the maid, A lin-g'ring fare-well tak - ing, Her
2. Then to the East we bore a-way, To win a name in sto - ry, And

sighs and tears my steps de - lay'd, I thought her heart was break - ing, In
there, where dawns the sun of day, There dawn'd our sun of glo - ry: Both

hur-ried words her name I bless'd, I breath'd the vows that bind me, And
blaz'd in noon on Al-ma's height, Where in the post as - sign'd me, I

to my heart in an-guish press'd, The girl I left be - hind me.
shar'd the glo - ry of that fight, Sweet girl I left be - hind me.

It Was Not So To Be

(Trumpeter of Sakkingen)

Victor Nessler

Andante con moto

1. How bad-ly is the course of life ad-
2. Grief, en-vy, hate, were mine in am-ple

just - ed, That where sweet ros-es bloom sharp thorns a - bound, What though the
meas - ure, A storm-tried, sad and wea - ry wan-d'rer I, I dreamt of

heart has dear - ly, fond-ly trust - ed, The hour of part-ing will at last come
peace and hours of tran-quil pleas - ure, When un - to thee my path-way led me

round. Of thy fond glanc-es, once I read the mean - ing, They spoke of
nigh. Then through my soul a flash of joy went gleam - ing, Fain would I

joy and hap - pi - ness for me: God bless thee, love, it was but i - dle
pledge my youth-ful life to thee: God bless thee, love, it was but i - dle

dream - ing, God bless thee, love, it was not so to be.____ God bless thee
dream - ing, God bless thee, love, it was not so to be.____ God bless thee

love, it was but i - dle dream - ing, God bless thee, love, it was not so to be.
love, it was but i - dle dream - ing, God bless thee, love, it was not so to be.

Love's The Tune
(A Waltz Dream)

Oscar Straus

Allegretto

1. O lay your cheek to mine, my dear, While
2. The flute a - lone sounds rath - er sad, But

flute and fid - dle ring out clear. The flute trills love pres - tis - si -
with the fid - dle 'tis not bad! Ah, love a - lone is ag - o -

mo, The fid - dle in a - da - gi - o! Yet
ny, But love to - geth - er, ec - sta - cy Life's

That Viennese Waltz

(A Waltz Dream)

Oscar Straus

Tempo di Valse Lente

1. As once in a fair gar-den fra-grant, I dreamed while the twi-light shades fell;____ Came sweet strains on soft breez-es va - grant, Al - lur-ing with rap-tur-ous spell.____ They ech-o'd a mu-sic en-tranc - ing, Part joy and part yearn-ing de - sire!____ They

2. I dreamed in that gar-den rose-bow-er'd, Yet now all my dreams had come true;____ And fair-est of blos-soms had flow - er'd, Be-side me, my sweet-heart, were you.____ The bright gold - en days Time had ban-ished, Of love and of spring and of joy!____ We

(The Waltz Dream)
con espressione

With breez-es vy - ing, soft as they sigh, Ten-der-ly sigh - ing, dream waltz, you

die! My love-born sor - row ech-oes your sighs, ___ Their sweetness bor - rows,

up-ward to rise! Spring's ar-dent yearn - ing, Joy's con-stant flame, Doubt to hope

turn - ing, Love is your name, One more joy cap - tur'd, ere ends the day,

One more hour rap - tur'd, love-liv'd in May; One more joy cap - tur'd, ere ends the

day, One more hour rap - tur'd, love-liv'd in May. I May.

Vilia Song
(The Merry Widow)

Franz Lehar

Andantino

mf A

Vil - ia, a wood nymph, her green home had made, 'Neath leaf shad-ow'd
In - to her bow - er the hunts-man she drew, Where green ver-dur'd

bow - ers in dim for-est glade, A hunts - man there spied her, for-
hang - ings a cool shad-ow threw, He knew the de - light of a

got was the chase; His eyes could not wea - ry of her love-ly face,
pas - sion a - bove, The ten - der-est rap - tures of mere earth-ly love;

While a strange de-light-ful thrill, Went ting-ling thro' his veins at
Till from his fond kiss-es torn, The maid-en sud-den-ly was

will, His sad sigh echoed thro' the for - est still.
gone, All in vain on the breeze his plea was borne.

Waltz Song
(The Merry Widow)

Franz Lehar

glide, Our souls drift with its tide, Hearts that were sad no

more re-pine, but joy - ous, cry, "Be mine!"___ And tho'

you smile si-lent-ly,___ There is an e-cho sings to me,___ "'Tis you a-lone I

love ___ e - ter - nal - ly!"___ Words are vain when

mu - sic's strain Says "Love me, do!"

When swift feet cry as they fleet "Love, I love

you!" When hands each oth - er press - ing,

With each clasp re - new, Vows that say "Dear

love, for aye, I'll love you true!"

The Flowers That Bloom In The Spring
(The Mikado)

Sir Arthur Sullivan

Poor Wand'ring One
(Pirates of Penzance)

Sir Arthur Sullivan

I'm Called Little Buttercup
(H.M.S. Pinafore)

Sir Arthur Sullivan

Tempo di Valse

Lullaby
(Erminie)

E. Jakobowski

1. Dear moth-er in dreams I see her,— With lov'd face sweet and calm,— And hear her voice with love re-joice, When nest-ling on her arm,— I think how she soft-ly press'd me, Of the tears in each glist-'ning eye,— As her watch she'd keep, When she rock'd to sleep, Her child to this lul-la-by— Bye, bye, bye, bye, bye, bye, bye, bye, Bye,

2. Ah! e'en when her life was eb-bing,— Her words were all of me,— My fu-ture years were all her fears, Her fate was not to see,— My fa-ther, I heard you weep-ing, As in sor-row you stand-ing by,— And my moth-er's plaint, In her ac-cents faint, This ten-der sweet lul-la-by— bye, bye, bye, bye, bye, bye,

Slowly

Tit-Willow
(The Mikado)

Sir Arthur Sullivan

Auld Lang Syne

ROBERT BURNS

Home Sweet Home

John Howard Payne

Henry C. Bishop

Moderato

1. 'Mid pleas - ures and pal - a - ces though we may roam, Be it
2. An ex - ile from home, splen-dor daz - zles in vain, Oh

ev - er so hum - ble, there's no place like home. A
give me my low - ly thatched cot - tage a - gain! The

charm from the skies seems to hal - low us there, Which
birds sing - ing gai - ly that came at my call, Give me

seek through the world, is not met with else - where.
them with that peace of mind, dear-er than all.

Home! Home! Sweet, sweet home! There's

no ____ place like | home, ____ there's | no ____ place like | home.

Sweet and Low

Joseph Barnby

Larghetto

1. Sweet and low, | sweet and low, | Wind of the West - ern | sea; ____ | Low, low,
2. Sleep and rest, | sleep and rest, | Fa-ther will come to thee | soon; ____ | Rest, rest on

breathe and blow, | Wind of the West - ern | sea; ____ | O-ver the roll - ing
moth - er's breast, | Fa-ther will come to thee | soon; ____ | Fa-ther will come to his

wa - ters go | Come from the dy - ing | moon and blow, | Blow him a-gain to
babe in the nest, | Sil - ver sails all | out of the West, | Un-der the sil - ver

me, ____ | While my lit-tle one, | while my pret-ty one | sleeps. ____
moon, ____ | Sleep my lit-tle one, | sleep my pret-ty one, | sleep. ____

Do They Think of Me at Home?

C.W. GLOVER

I Cannot Sing the Old Songs

CLARIBEL

The Old Oaken Bucket

S. WOODWORTH

KIALLMARK

cot of my fa-ther, the dai-ry house by it, And
soon with the em-blem of truth o-ver-flow-ing, And
fan-cy re-verts to my fa-ther's plan-ta-tion, And

e'en the rude buck-et that hung in the well. The
drip-ping with cool-ness it rose from the well. The
sighs for the buck-et that hung in the well. The

CHORUS

old oak-en buck-et, the i-ron-bound bucket, The moss-cover'd buck-et that hung in the well.

The Old Folks at Home

S.C. FOSTER

Moderato

1. Way down up-on de Swa-nee rib-ber, Far, far a-way,
2. All 'round de lit-tle farm I wan-der'd When I was young,
3. One lit-tle hut a-mong de bush-es, One dat I love,

Dere's wha my heart is turn-ing eb-ber, Dere's wha de old folks stay.
Den ma-ny hap-py days I squan-der'd, Ma-ny de songs I sung.
Still sad-ly to my mem-'ry rush-es, No mat-ter where I rove.

Three Fishers Went Sailing

CHARLES KINGSLEY

J. HULLAH

Silver Threads Among The Gold

H. P. Danks

Chorus

mf

Dar - ling, I am grow-ing, grow-ing old, Sil - ver threads a - mong the gold,

Shine up-on my brow to - day, _____ Life is fad-ing fast a - way. _____

Grandfather's Clock

Henry C. Work

Moderato

mf

1. My grand - fa - ther's clock was too large for the shelf, So it
2. In watch - ing its pen - du - lum swing to and fro, Man - y
3. My grand - fa - ther said that of those he could hire, Not a
4. It rang an a - larm in the dead of the night An a -

stood nine-ty years on the floor; _____ It was tall - er by half than the
hours had he spent while a boy; _____ And in child - hood and man - hood the
ser - vant so faith - ful he found; _____ For it wa - sted no time, and had
larm that for years had been dumb; _____ And we knew that his spir - it was

mf

old man him - self, Though it weighed not a pen - ny-weight more. _____ It was
clock seem'd to know And to share both his grief and his joy. _____ For it
but one de - sire At the close of each week to be wound. _____ And it
plum - ing for flight, That his hour of de - par-ture had come. _____ Still the

Song of the Volga Boatmen

Russian Folk Song

Heave a - way, Heave a - way, Let us pull with

vim once more! Heave a - way, Heave a - way,

Let us pull with vim once more! See the tall trees

draw - ing nigh, Pull, and soon we'll pass them by;

Yankee Doodle

The Star Spangled Banner

FRANCIS SCOTT KEY

JOHN S. SMITH

air, Gave proof thro' the night that our flag was still there.
beam, In full glo - ry re - flect - ed now shines in the stream:
slave From the ter - ror of flight or the gloom of the grave.
just, And this be our mot - to, "In God is our trust."

Chorus

Oh! say, does that star spangled banner yet wave, O'er the land of the free and the home of the brave!

SAMUEL FRANCIS SMITH   America   HENRY CAREY

Maestoso

1. My coun - try, 'tis of thee, Sweet land of lib - er - ty,
2. My na - tive coun - try, thee, Land of the no - ble free,
3. Let mus - ic swell the breeze, And ring from all the trees,
4. Our fa - ther's God! to Thee, Au - thor of lib - er - ty,

Of thee I sing; Land where my fa - thers died; Land of the
Thy name I love; I love thy rocks and rills, Thy woods and
Sweet free - dom's song; Let mor - tal tongues a - wake, Let all that
To Thee we sing; Long may our land be bright, With free - dom's

pil - grim's pride; From ev - 'ry moun - tain side Let free - dom ring.
tem - pled hills; My heart with rap - ture thrills, Like that a - bove.
breathe par - take; Let rocks their si - lence break, The sound pro - long.
ho - ly light; Pro - tect us by Thy might, Great God, our King.

Hail, Columbia

J. HOPKINSON

P. PHILE

The Red, White and Blue

D. T. SHAW

THOMAS A BECKET

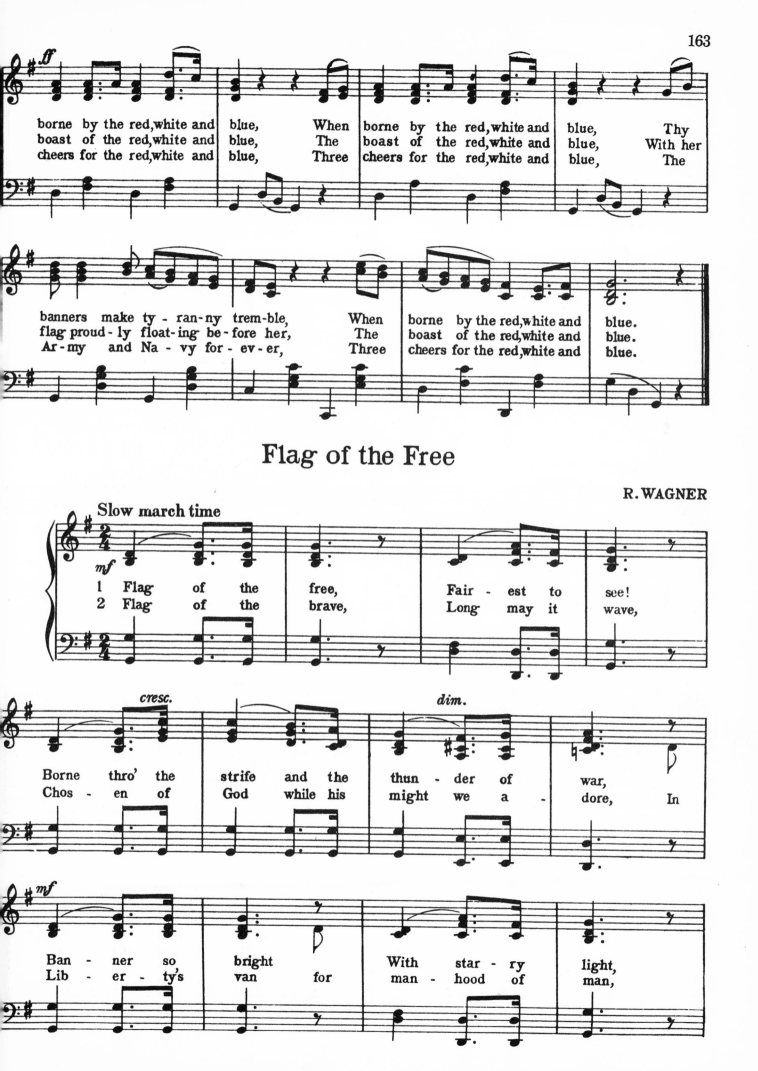

Flag of the Free

R. WAGNER

Slow march time

borne by the red, white and blue, When borne by the red, white and blue, Thy
boast of the red, white and blue, The boast of the red, white and blue, With her
cheers for the red, white and blue, Three cheers for the red, white and blue, The

banners make ty - ran - ny trem - ble, When borne by the red, white and blue.
flag proud - ly float - ing be - fore her, The boast of the red, white and blue.
Ar - my and Na - vy for - ev - er, Three cheers for the red, white and blue.

1 Flag of the free, Fair - est to see!
2 Flag of the brave, Long may it wave,

Borne thro' the strife and the thun - der of war,
Chos - en of God while his might we a - dore, In

Ban - ner so bright With star - ry light,
Lib - er - ty's van for man - hood of man,

We're Tenting To-Night

WALTER KITTREDGE

see the dawn of peace. Tent - ing to - night.

cresc.

Tent - ing to - night,

Ending for Verses 1.2.3.

tent - ing on the old camp ground.

Ending for Verse 4.

Dy - ing on the old camp ground.

Tramp! Tramp! Tramp!

GEORGE F. ROOT

Moderato

mf

1. In the pris - on cell I sit, Think-ing, Moth - er dear of you, And our
2. In the bat - tle front we stood When their fierc - est charge they made, And they
3. So, with - in the pris - on cell, We are wait - ing for the day, That shall

bright and hap - py home so far a - way; And the
swept us off a hun - dred men or more; But be -
come to o - pen wide the i - ron door, And the

tears they fill my eyes, Spite of all that I can do, Though I
fore we reached their lines, They were beat - en back, dis - mayed, And we
hol - low eye grows bright, And the poor heart al - most gay, As we

try to cheer my com - rades and be gay.
heard the cry of vic - t'ry o'er and o'er.
think of see - ing home and friends once more.

CHORUS

Tramp! tramp! tramp! the boys are march - ing,

Cheer up, com - rades, they will come, And be - neath the star - ry flag We shall

breathe the air a - gain Of the free land in our own, be - lov - ed home.

When Johnny Comes Marching Home

P. S. GILMORE

March time

1. When John-ny comes march-ing home a-gain, Hur-rah, _____ hur-
2. The old_ church bell will peal with joy, Hur-rah, _____ hur-
3. Get read-y for the Ju-bi-lee, Hur-rah, _____ hur-
4. Let love_ and friend-ship on that day, Hur-rah, _____ hur-

rah! _____ We'll give him a heart-y wel-come then, Hur-
rah! _____ To wel-come home our dar-ling boy, Hur-
rah! _____ We'll give_ the he-ro three times three, Hur-
rah! _____ Their choic-est treas-ures then dis-play, Hur-

rah, _____ hur-rah! _____ The_ men will cheer,_ the
rah, _____ hur-rah! _____ The_ vil-lage lads_ and
rah, _____ hur-rah! _____ The_ lau-rel wreath_ is
rah, _____ hur-rah! _____ And_ let each one_ per-

boys will shout, The la-dies they_ will all turn out, And we'll
las-sies say, With ro-ses they_ will strew the way, And we'll
read-y now, To place up-on_ his loy-al brow, And we'll
form some part, To fill with joy_ the war-rior's heart, And we'll

all feel gay, when John-ny comes march-ing home. _____

Battle Hymn of the Republic

Julia Ward Howe

William Steffe

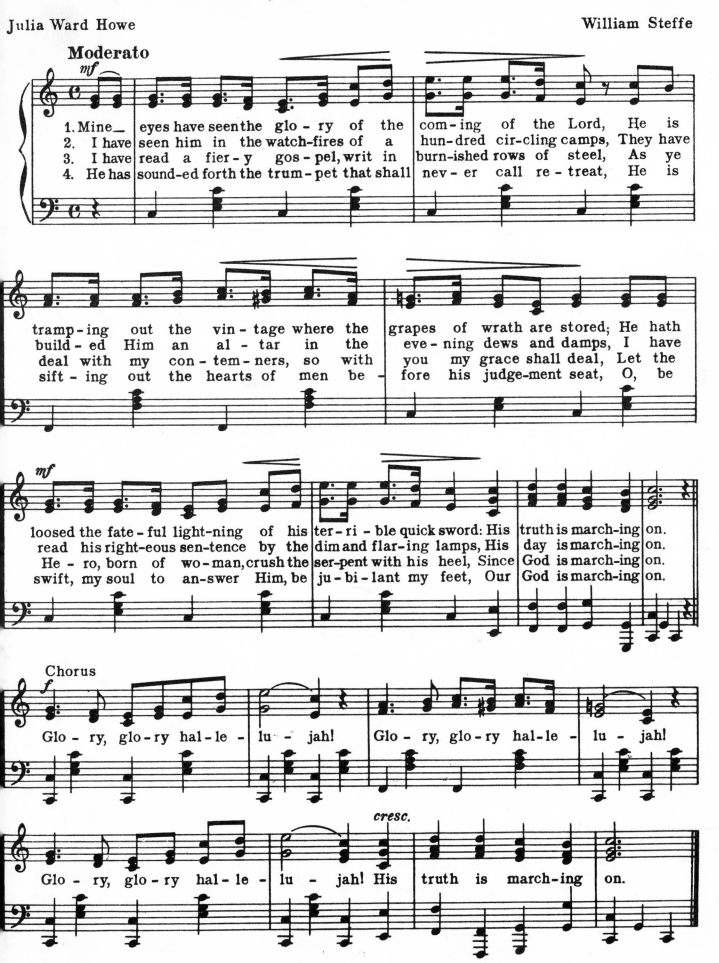

Moderato

1. Mine__ eyes have seen the glo - ry of the com - ing of the Lord, He is
2. I have seen him in the watch-fires of a hun - dred cir - cling camps, They have
3. I have read a fier - y gos - pel, writ in burn-ished rows of steel, As ye
4. He has sound-ed forth the trum - pet that shall nev - er call re - treat, He is

tramp - ing out the vin - tage where the grapes of wrath are stored; He hath
build - ed Him an al - tar in the eve - ning dews and damps, I have
deal with my con - tem - ners, so with you my grace shall deal, Let the
sift - ing out the hearts of men be - fore his judge-ment seat, O, be

loosed the fate - ful light - ning of his ter - ri - ble quick sword: His truth is march-ing on.
read his right-eous sen - tence by the dim and flar-ing lamps, His day is march-ing on.
He - ro, born of wo - man, crush the ser-pent with his heel, Since God is march-ing on.
swift, my soul to an - swer Him, be ju - bi - lant my feet, Our God is march-ing on.

Chorus

Glo - ry, glo - ry hal - le - lu - jah! Glo - ry, glo - ry hal - le - lu - jah!

cresc.

Glo - ry, glo - ry hal - le - lu - jah! His truth is march-ing on.

The Battle Cry Of Freedom

Geo. F. Root

Listen to the Mocking Bird

ALICE HAWTHORNE
(Septimus Winner)

mock-ing bird, Lis-ten to the mock-ing bird, The mocking bird still singing o'er her

grave: Lis-ten to the mock-ing bird, Lis-ten to the

mock-ing bird, Still sing-ing where the weep-ing wil-lows wave.

When You and I Were Young, Maggie

G. W. JOHNSON

J. A. BUTTERFIELD

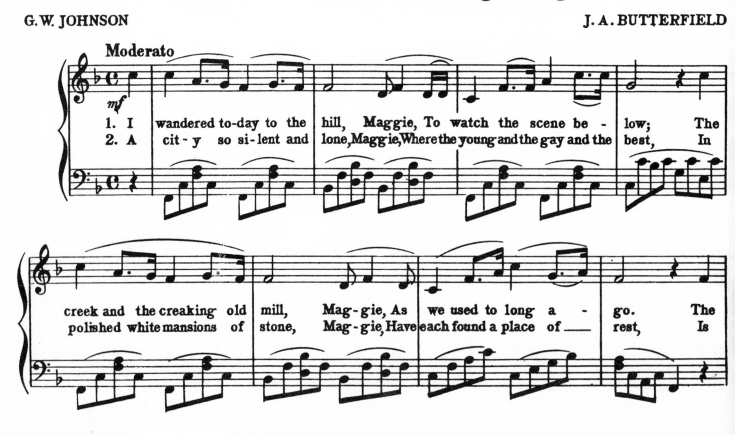

1. I wandered to-day to the hill, Maggie, To watch the scene be-low; The
2. A cit-y so si-lent and lone, Maggie, Where the young and the gay and the best, In

creek and the creaking old mill, Mag-gie, As we used to long a-go. The
polished white mansions of stone, Mag-gie, Have each found a place of rest, Is

green grove is gone from the hill, Mag-gie, Where first the dai - sies
built where the birds used to play, Mag-gie, And join in the songs that were

sprung; The creak - ing old mill is still, Mag-gie, Since
sung; For we sang as gay as they, Mag - gie, When

you and — I were young. And now we are a - ged and
you and — I were young. And now we are a - ged and

gray, Mag-gie, And the tri - als of life near-ly done; Let us

sing of the days that are gone, Mag-gie, When you and I were young.

The Poor Old Slave

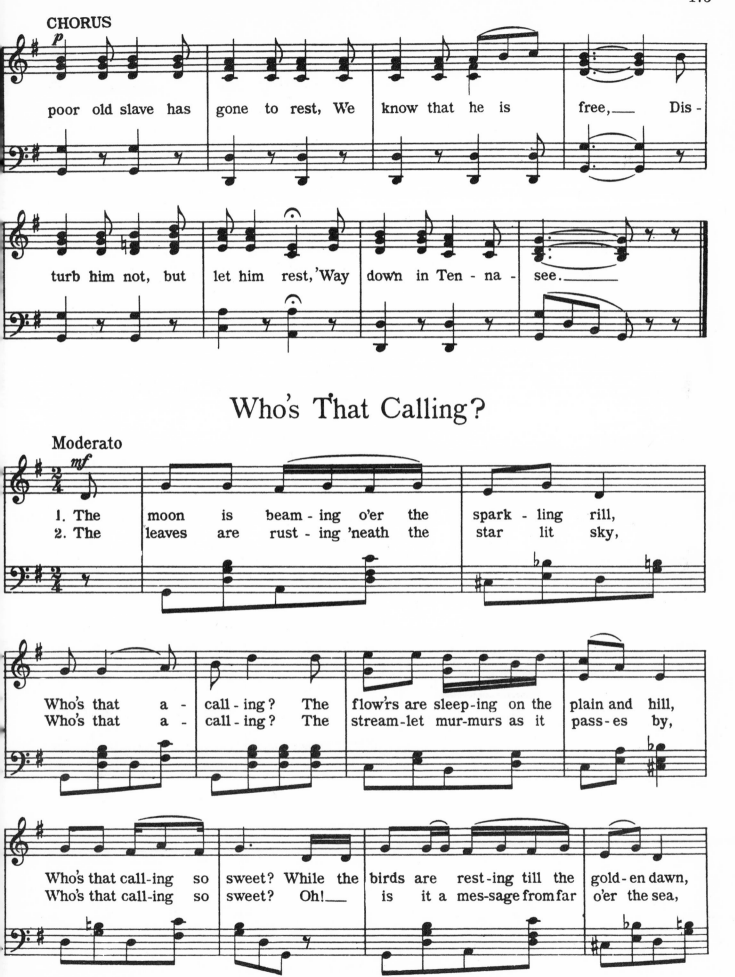

CHORUS

poor old slave has gone to rest, We know that he is free,____ Dis-
turb him not, but let him rest, 'Way down in Ten - na - see.____

Who's That Calling?

Moderato

1. The moon is beam - ing o'er the spark - ling rill,
2. The leaves are rust - ing 'neath the star lit sky,

Who's that a - call - ing? The flow'rs are sleep-ing on the plain and hill,
Who's that a - call - ing? The stream-let mur-murs as it pass-es by,

Who's that call-ing so sweet? While the birds are rest-ing till the gold-en dawn,
Who's that call-ing so sweet? Oh!___ is it a mes-sage from far o'er the sea,

The Old Cabin Home

Oh! Dem Golden Slippers!

J. A. BLAND

CHORUS

Oh, dem gold-en slip-pers! Oh, dem gold-en slip-pers!

Gold-en slip-pers I'se gwine to wear, be-kase dey look so neat,

Oh, dem gold-en slip-pers! Oh, dem gold-en slip-pers!

Gold-en slip-pers I'se gwine to wear, to walk de gold-en street. street.

Uncle Ned

S. C. FOSTER

Moderato

1. Dere was an old nig-ga, dey call'd him Un-cle Ned, He's__
2. His fin-gers were long like de cane__ in de brake, He__
3. When ole__ Ned die Mas-sa took it migh-ty hard, De__

dead long a-go, long a- go; He had no wool on de top ob his head De
had no eyes for to see; He had no teeth for to eat de corn cake, So he
tears run down like de rain; Ole Missus turn pale and she gets ber-ry sad, Cayse she

place whar de wool ought to grow. Den lay down de shub-ble and de hoe.
had to let de corn cake be. Den lay down de shub-ble and de hoe.
neb-ber see Ole Ned a - gain. Den lay down de shub-ble and de hoe.

slowly   *rit.*

CHORUS
mp

Hang up de fid-dle and de bow: For there's no more work for

poor Old Ned He's gone whar de good nig-gas go.

Zip Coon
(Turkey in the Straw)

Lively

1. I went down to San-dy Hook de od-er ar-ter-noon, I went down to San-dy Hook de
2. Ole Su - key Blue - skin fell in lub wid me, Ole Su - key Blue - skin

Maryland! My Maryland!

JAMES R. RANDALL

Melody, "O Tannenbaum"

Moderato

1. Thou wilt not cow-er in the dust, Ma-ry-land! my Ma-ry-land!
2. Thou wilt not yield the Van-dal toil, Ma-ry-land! my Ma-ry-land!
3. I see no blush up-on thy cheek, Ma-ry-land! my Ma-ry-land!
4. I hear the dis-tant thun-der hum, Ma-ry-land! my Ma-ry-land!

Thy beam-ing sword shall nev-er rust, Ma-ry-land! my Ma-ry-land!
Thou wilt not crook to his con-trol, Ma-ry-land! my Ma-ry-land!
Tho' thou wast ev-er brave-ly meek, Ma-ry-land! my Ma-ry-land!
The Old Line bu-gle, fife and drum, Ma-ry-land! my Ma-ry-land!

Re-mem-ber Car-roll's sa-cred trust, Re-mem-ber How-ard's war-like thrust,
Bet-ter the fire up-on thee roll, Bet-ter the shot, the blade, the bowl,
For life and death. for woe and weal, Thy peer-less chiv-al-ry re-veal,
Come! to thine own he-ro-ic throng, That stalks with Lib-er-ty a-long,

And all thy slum-b'rers with the just, Ma-ry-land! my Ma-ry-land!
Than cru-ci-fix-ion of the soul, Ma-ry-land! my Ma-ry-land!
And gird thy beau-teous limbs with steel, Ma-ry-land! my Ma-ry-land!
And ring thy daunt-less slo-gan song, Ma-ry-land! my Ma-ry-land!

Polly-Wolly-Doodle

4 Oh, a grass-hopper sittin' on a railroad track
A-pickin' his teef wid a carpet tack.

5 Oh, I went to bed, but it wasn't no use,
My feet stuck out for a chicken roost.

6 Behind de barn, down on my knees
I thought I heard that chicken sneeze.

7 He sneezed so hard wid de 'hoopin cough,
He sneezed his head an' tail right off.

Cornfield Medley

Kingdom Coming

H. C. WORK

mus' be now de king-dom com-in' An' de year ob Ju-bi-lo!

Rosa Lee

Lively
mf

1. When I lib'd in Ten-nes-see, U-li-a-li o-la-e,
2. I said you lub-ly gal dat's plain, U-li-a-li o-la-e,
3. My sto-ry yet is to be told U-li-a-li o-la-e,

I went court-in' Ro-sa Lee, U-li-a-li o-la-e,
Breff as sweet as su-gar cane, U-li-a-li o-la-e,
Ro-sa cotch'd a shock-ing cold, U-li-a-li o-la-e,

Eyes as dark as win-ter night; Lips as red— as— ber-riés bright, When
Feet so large and come-ly too, Might make a— cra-dle of each shoe; —
Send de doc-tor, fetch de nurse, Doc-tor came, but— made her worse, I

first I did her woo-ing go, She said, "Now don't be fool-ish Joe."
Ro-sa, take me for your beau, She said, "Now don't be fool-ish Joe."
tried to make her laugh, but no She said, "Fare-well, my dear-est Joe!"

I'se Gwine Back To Dixie

MINSTREL BALLAD

Sally, Come Up.

Come Where My Love Lies Dreaming

STEPHEN C. FOSTER

Come where my love lies dream - ing, Dream - ing the hap-py hours a -

way; In vis - ions bright re - deem - ing The fleet - ing joys of

day. Dream - ing the hap - py hours,

Dream - ing the hap-py hours a - way, Come where my love lies

dream - ing, Yes, is sweet-ly dream - ing the hap-py hours a - way.

Interlude

mf

Come with a lute, come with a lay, My own love is sweet-ly

dream - ing, Her beauty beaming; Come where my love lies

dreaming, Yes, is sweetly dream-ing the hap-py hours a - way.

Interlude

mf

My Old Kentucky Home.

STEPHEN C. FOSTER

Moderato.

1. The sun shines bright in the old Ken-tuck-y home, 'Tis sum-mer the dark - ies are gay;
2. They hunt no more for the pos-sum and the coon, On the mead-ow, the hill and the shore;
3. The head must bow and the back will have to bend, Wher - ev - er the dark - ey may go;

The corn top's ripe and the mead-ow's in the bloom, While the birds make mu-sic all the day.
They sing no more by the glim - mer of the moon, On the bench by the old cab - in door.
A few more days and the trou - ble all will end, In the fields where the su-gar canes grow.

The young folks roll on the lit - tle cab-in floor, all mer - ry, all hap - py and bright;
The day goes by like a shad-ow o'er the heart, with sor - row, where all was de - light;
A few more days for to tote the wea-ry load, no mat - ter 'twill nev - er be light;

By'n - bye hard times comes a knock - ing at the door, Then my old Ken-tuck - y home, good night.
The time has come when the dark - ies have to part, Then my old Ken-tuck - y home, good night.
A few more days 'til we tot - ter on the road, Then my old Ken-tuck - y home, good night.

CHORUS.

Weep no more, my la - dy, Oh, weep no more to - day! We will

sing one song for the old Ken-tuck-y home, For the old Ken-tuck-y home far a - way.

Dixie Land.

DAN EMMET.

Quickly.

1. { I wish I was in de land ob cot - ton, Old times dar am
{ In Dix - ie land whar I was born in, Ear - ly on one

2. { Old Miss - us Ma - ry "Will - de - wea - ber," Will - ium was a
{ But when he put his arms a - round 'er, He smiled as fierce as a

3. { His face was sharp as a butch - er's clea - ver, But soon af - ter
{ Old Miss - us act - ed de fool - ish part And died for a man

not for-got - ten, Look a - way, look a - way, look a - way, Dix-ie Land.
frost - y morn - in', Look a - way, look a - way, look a - way, Dix-ie Land.
gay de - cea - ber; Look a - way, look a - way, look a - way, Dix-ie Land.
for - ty pound - er, Look a - way, look a - way, look a - way, Dix-ie Land.
he did leave 'er; Look a - way, look a - way, look a - way, Dix-ie Land.
dat broke her heart, Look a - way, look a - way, look a - way, Dix-ie Land.

4. Now here's a health to the next old Missus,
And all de gals dat want to kiss us,
Look away! etc.
But if you want to drive 'way sorrow,
Come and hear dis song to-morrow
Look away! etc.

5. Dar's buckwheat cakes an' Ingen batter,
Makes you fat or a little fatter,
Look away! etc.
Den hoe it down an' scratch you grabble,
To Dixie's land I'm bound to trabble,
Look away! etc.

Camptown Races

(Gwine to Run All Night)

S.C. FOSTER

1. De Camp-town la-dies sing dis song, Doo-dah! doo-dah! De Camptown race track
2. De long-tail filly and de big black horse, Doo-dah! doo-dah! Dey fly de track an dey
3. Old mu-ley cow come on to de track, Doo-dah! doo-dah! De bob-tail flung her

five miles long, Oh! doo-dah day! I come down dah wid my hat caved in,
both cut across, Oh! doo-dah day! De blind hoss sticken in a big mud hole,
ov-erhisback, Oh! doo-dah day!

Doo-dah! doo-dah! I go back home wid a pock-et full of tin, Oh! Doo-dah day!
Doo-dah! doo-dah! Can't touch bot-tom wid a ten-foot pole, Oh! Doo-dah day!

Chorus

Gwine to run all night! Gwine to run all day! I'll

bet my mon-ey on a bob-tail nag, Some-bod-y bet on de bay.

Hard Times Come Again No More

S. C. FOSTER

Moderato

1. Let us pause in life's pleas-ures and count its man-y tears While we
2. Vhile we seek mirth and beau-ty and mu-sic light and gay There are
3. There's a pale, droop-ing maid-en who toils her life a-way, With a

all sup sor-row with the poor; There's a song that will ling-er for-
frail forms faint-ing at the door; Tho' their voices are si-lent, their plead-
worn heart whose bet-ter days are o'er; Tho' her voice would be mer-ry 'tis

ev-er in our ears, "Oh! Hard Times, come a-gain no more!"
ing looks will say, "Oh! Hard Times, come a-gain no more!" 'Tis the
sigh-ing all the day, "Oh! Hard Times, come a-gain no more!"

CHORUS

cresc

song, the sigh of the wea-ry; Hard Times! Hard Times! come a-gain no more! Man-y

days you have lin-gered a-round my cab-in door! Oh! Hard Times, come a-gain no more!"

Massa's In De Cold Ground

S. C. FOSTER

1. Round de mead-ows am a - ring - ing, De dark - ey's mourn-ful song,
2. When de au-tumn leaves were fall - ing, When de days were cold, 'Twas
3. Mas - sa make de dark - eys love him, Cayse he was so kind,

While de mock-ing bird am sing - ing, Hap-py as de day am long,
hard to hear old mas-sa call - ing, Cayse he was so weak and old,
Now, dey sad-ly weeps a - bove him, Mourning cayse he leave dem be-hind, I

Where de i - vy am a creep - ing, O'er de grass-y mound,
Now de or-ange tree am bloom - ing, On de sand-y shore,
Can - not work be-fore to mor - row, Cayse de tear-drop flow, I

Dare old mas-sa am a sleep-ing, Sleep-ing in de cold, cold ground.
Now de sum-mer days am com - ing, Mas-sa neb-ber calls no more. Back in de corn-field,
try to drive a-way my sor - row, Pick-in on de old ban-jo.

Hear dat mourn-ful sound; All de darkies am a weep - ing, Massa's in de cold, cold ground.

Ring, Ring De Banjo

S. C. FOSTER

Oh! Susanna

Old Black Joe

S. C. FOSTER

Andante espressivo

1. Gone are the days when my heart was young and gay,
2. Why do I weep when my heart should feel no pain?
3. Where are the hearts once so hap-py and so free? The

Gone are my friends from the cot-ton fields a-way;
Why do I sigh that my friends come not a-gain?
chil-dren, so dear, that I held up-on my knee?

Gone from the earth to a bet-ter land, I know, I
Griev-ing for forms now de-part-ed long a-go? I
Gone to the shore where my soul has longed to go, I

hear their gen-tle voi-ces call-ing "Old Black Joe!"
hear their gen-tle voi-ces call-ing "Old Black Joe!" } I'm coming, I'm com-ing, For my
hear their gen-tle voi-ces call-ing "Old Black Joe!"

CHORUS

head is bend-ing low; I hear those gen-tle voi-ces call-ing "Old Black Joe!"

Old Dog Tray

S. C. FOSTER

Beautiful Dreamer

STEPHEN C. FOSTER

Beautiful dream - er,   wake un-to me,   Starlight and dewdrops are wait-ing for
Beautiful dream - er,   out on the sea,   Mermaids are chanting the wild lo - re -

thee, _____   Sounds of the rude   world   heard in the day,
lei, _____   O - ver the stream - let   va - pors are borne,

Lull'd by the moonlight have all pass'd a -   way! _____   Beau - ti - ful dream - er,
Wait - ing to fade at the bright com-ing   morn. _____   Beau - ti - ful dream - er,

queen of my song,   List while I woo   thee, with soft mel - o - dy;
beam on my heart,   E'en as the morn   on   the streamlet and sea;

Gone are the cares   of   life's bu-sy throng,   Beau - ti - ful dreamer, awake un - to
Then will all clouds   of   sor-row de - part,   Beau - ti - ful dreamer, awake un - to

me! _____ Beau-ti-ful dream-er, a wake un-to me.

Under The Willow She's Sleeping

Stephen C. Foster

Andante

mf

1. Un-der the wil-low she's laid with care ___ (Sang a lone moth-er while weeping,)
2. Un-der the wil-low no songs are heard, Near where my dar-ling lies dreaming;

Un-der the wil - low, with gold - en hair, My dar-ling is qui-et-ly sleeping.
Nought but the voice of some far - off bird, Where life and its pleasures are beaming.

Chorus

f

Fair, fair, with gold - en hair, (Sang a lone moth-er while weeping,) ___

Fair, fair, with gold - en hair, Un-der the wil - low she's sleeping. ___

Nelly Was A Lady

Stephen C. Foster

Oh! Boys Carry Me 'Long

Stephen C. Foster

The Glendy Burke

Stephen C. Foster

Allegro

1. De Glen-dy Burke is a might-y fast boat, wid a might-y fast cap-tain too; He
2. De Glen-dy Burke has a fun-ny old crew, and dey sing de boat-man's song; Dey

sets up dar on de hur-ri-cane roof, And he keeps his eye on de crew. I
burn de pitch an' de pine knot too, For to shove de boat a - long. De

can't stay here, for de work's too hard, I'm bound to leave dis town; I'll
smoke goes up an' de in - jine roars, An' de wheel goes round an' round; So

take my duds an' tote 'em on my back, When de Glen-dy Burke comes down.
fare ye well, for I'll take a lit-tle ride, When de Glen-dy Burke comes down.

Chorus

Ho! for Lou' - si - an - a! I'm bound to leave this town; I'll

take my duds an' tote 'em on my back, When de Glen - dy Burke comes down.

Jeanie With The Light Brown Hair

Stephen C. Foster

Moderato

1. I dream of Jea-nie with the light brown hair, Borne like a va - por on the sum-mer air, I see her trip-ping where the bright streams play, Hap-py as the dai-sies that dance on her way, Man-y were the wild notes her mer- ry voice would pour, Man-y were the blithe birds that war- bled them o'er. Oh! I dream of Jea-nie with the light brown hair, Float-ing like a va-por on the soft sum-mer air.

2. I long for Jea-nie with the day— dawn smile, Ra - dia-ting glad-ness warm with win-ning guile; I hear her mel - o - dies, like joys gone by, Sigh-ing round my heart o'er the fond hopes that die, Sigh-ing like the night wind and sob-bing like the rain, Wait-ing for the lost one that comes not a - gain. Oh! I long for Jea-nie and my heart bows low, Nev- er-more to find her where the bright wa-ters flow.

Nelly Bly

S. C. Foster

sing for you, play for you, a dul - cem mel - o - dy.

Heigh! Nel - ly! Ho! Nel - ly! lis - ten, lub, to me, I'll

sing for you, play for you, a dul - cem mel - o - dy.

I Want To See The Old Home

James E. Stewart

Moderato *mf*

1. I've wan - dered ve - ry far a - way, From the clime where I was born,____ And my poor heart has been so sad, de - ject - ed and for -
2. I'm left all sad and lone - ly now, When my days are ve - ry few,____ My wife and chil - dren both are gone, I don't know what to
3. When I was free, I left that land, Where the days are bright and fair,____ Where mis - sus spoke to me so kind, When I was bow'd with

Jingle Bells

Dear Evelina, Sweet Evelina

Allegretto

1. Way down in the mead-ow where the li - ly first blows, Where the
2. She's fair as a rose, like a ___ lamb she is meek, And she
3. Ev-e - li - na and I one fine ___ eve-ning in June, Took a

wind from the moun-tains ne'er ruf - fles ___ the ___ rose; Lives ___
nev - er was known to put paint on ___ her ___ cheek, In the
walk all a - lone by the light of ___ the ___ moon, The ___

fond Ev - e - li - na, the sweet lit - tle dove, The
most grace - ful curls 'hangs her ra - ven black hair, And she
plan - ets all shone for the heav - ens were clear, And I

pride of the val - ley, the girl that I love.
nev - er re - quires ___ per - fum - er - y there.
felt round the heart most tre - men - dous - ly queer.

CHORUS

Dear Ev - e - li - na, sweet Ev - e - li - na,

My love for thee shall nev - er, nev-er die.

Dear Ev - e - li - na, sweet Ev - e - li - na,

My love for thee shall nev - er, nev-er die.

Forty-Nine Bottles

Moderato

cresc.

1   For-ty-nine bot-tles hanging on the wall,   For-ty-nine bot-tles hanging on the wall,
2, 3 etc Forty-eight bot-tles   etc

dim.

Take one a - way   from them all,   For - ty- eight bot - tles   hang-ing on the wall.

Funiculi, Funicula

L. DENZA

Forsaken

THOMAS KOSCHAT

1 For - sa-ken, for-sa-ken, for - sa - ken am I, Like a stone on the
2 Near a knoll in the for-est, where sweet flow-ers bloom, My sweetheart is

pathway, neg - lect-ed I lie To the churchyard there yon-der so sad - ly I go And
sleeping, in mossy cov-er'd tomb So there oft-en I wan-der to weep and to sigh And

there low-ly kneeling I pour out my woe, And there low-ly kneeling I pour out my woe.
mur-mur to her there "For - sa-ken am I" And mur-mur to her there "For - sa-ken am I."

Go To Sleep, Lena Darling
(EMMET'S LULLABY)

J. K. EMMET

1 Close your eyes, Le - na, my dar - ling While I sing your lul - la -
2 Bright be de morn - ing, my dar - ling, Ven you ope your eyes;

by; fear thou no dan-ger Le - na, Move not, dear Le - na, my dar - ling;
Sunbeams glow all round you Le - na, Peace be with thee, love, my dar - ling;

For your brooder watch-es nigh you, Le - na, dear. An - gels guide thee,
Blue and cloudless be the sky for Le - na dear. Birds sing their bright

Le - na dear, my dar - ling__ Noth - ing e - vil can come near;
songs for thee, my dar - ling__ Full of sweet - est mel - o - dy;

Bright - est flow - ers blow for thee, Dar - ling sis - ter, dear to me.
An - gels ev - er hov - er near, Dar - ling sis - ter, dear to me.

CHORUS

Go to sleep, go to sleep, my ba - by, my ba - by, my ba - by;

Go to sleep, my ba - by__ ba - by, oh bye! Go to __ sleep, Le - na, sleep.

Good-Bye, My Lover, Good-Bye

Vive l'Amour

Lively

1. Let ev-'ry good fel-low now fill up his glass, Vi-ve la com-pag-nie, And
2. Let ev-er-y mar-ried man drink to his wife, Vi-ve la com-pag-nie, The
3. Come fill up your glass-es, I'll give you a toast, Vi-ve la com-pag-nie, Here's a
4. I hope it will please you to drink now with me, Vi-ve la com-pag-nie, I

drink to the health of our glo-ri-ous class, Vi-ve la com-pag-nie.
joy of his bo-som and plague of his life, Vi-ve la com-pag-nie.
health to our friend, our kind wor-thy host, Vi-ve la com-pag-nie.
hope it will please you to drink now with me, Vi-ve la com-pag-nie.

Vi-ve la, vi-ve la, vi-ve l'a-mour, Vi-ve la, vi-ve la, vi-ve l'a-mour,

vi-ve l'a-mour, vi-ve l'a-mour, vi-ve la com-pag-nie!

Oh My Darling Clementine

PERCY MONTROSE

5

In a churchyard near the canon,
Where the myrtle doth entwine,
There grow roses and other posies,
Fertilized by Clementine.

6

Then the miner, forty-niner,
Soon began to peak and pine,
Thought he "oughter jine" his daughter,
Now he's with his Clementine.

7

In my dreams she still doth haunt me
Robed in garments soaked in brine,
Though in life I used to hug her,
Now she's dead, I'll draw the line.

Over the Banister

Sailing

GODFREY MARKS

With Spirit

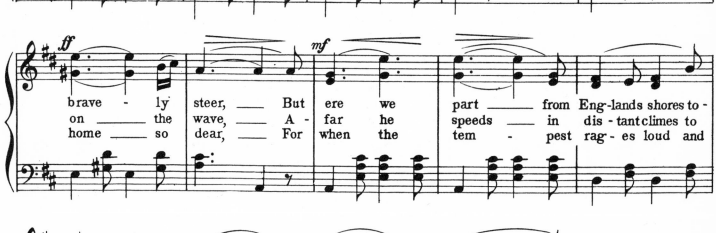

Then here's to the sail - or, and here's to the heart so true, Who will think of him up-

on the wa - ters blue! Sail - ing sail - ing o - ver the bounding

CHORUS

main ___ For man-y a storm-y wind shall blow ere Jack comes home a - gain! ___

Sail - ing, sail - ing, o - ver the bound - ing main: ___ For

man-y a storm-y wind shall blow, ere Jack comes home a - gain. ___

Solomon Levi

Moderato

1. My name is Sol-o-mon Le - vi, At my store on Sa - lem
2. And if a bum - mer comes a - long To my store on Sa - lem

street, __ That's where you'll buy your coats and vests, And
street, __ And tries to hang me up for coats, And

ev - 'ry - thing that's neat; __ I've sec - ond - hand - ed
vests so ve - ry neat; __ I kicks the bum - mer right

Ul - ster - ettes, And ev - 'ry - thing that's fine, __ For __
out of my store And on him sets my pup, __ For I

all the boys, __ they trade with me, At a hun-dred and for - ty nine. __
won't sell cloth-ing to an - y man Who tries __ to set me up. __

From "College Songs" by arr. with the Oliver Ditson Co.

Chorus

O, Sol-o-mon Le - vi! Le - vi! tra la la la! ___ Poor cheen-y Le - vi!

Tra la la la la la la la la la, ___ My name is Sol-o-mon Le - vi, At my store on Sa - lem

street; That's where you'll buy your coats and vests, And ev-'ry-thing else that's neat; ___

Sec - ond-hand - ed Ul - ster-ettes and ev-'ry-thing else that's fine, ___ For

all the boys they trade with me At a hun-dred and for - ty - nine. ___

The Quilting Party

Moderato

1. In the sky the bright stars glit-tered, —— On the bank the pale moon
2. On my arm a soft hand rest-ed, —— Rest-ed light as o - cean
3. On my lips a whis - per trembled, —— Trembled 'til it dared to

shone; And 'twas from Aunt Di-nah's quilting par-ty I was see - ing Nel-lie
foam; And 'twas from Aunt Di-nah's quilting par-ty I was see - ing Nel-lie
come, And 'twas from Aunt Di-nah's quilting par-ty I was see - ing Nel-lie

Chorus

home.
home. I was see-ing Nel-lie home, —— I was see-ing Nel-lie home. And 'twas
home.

from Aunt Di - nah's quilt - ing par - ty I was see - ing Nel - lie home.

Good-Night, Ladies

Moderato

1. Good - night, la - dies! —— Good - night, la - dies! —— Good - night,
2. Fare - well, la - dies! —— Fare - well, la - dies! —— Fare - well,
3. Sweet dreams, la - dies! —— Sweet dreams, la - dies! —— Sweet dreams,

la - dies! —— We're going to leave you now.

Allegro

Mer - ri - ly we roll a - long,

Third Verse P

roll a-long, roll a-long, Mer-ri-ly we roll a-long O'er the dark blue sea.

Juanita

Andante

1. Soft o'er the foun-tain, ling-'ring falls the south-ern moon,
2. When in thy dream-ing, moons like these shall shine a-gain,

Far o'er the moun-tain Breaks the day too soon! In thy dark eyes
And day-light beam-ing Prove thy dreams are vain, Wilt thou not re-

splen-dor Where the warm light loves to dwell, Wear-y looks yet ten-der,
lent-ing, For thine ab-sent lov-er sigh, In thy heart con-sent-ing

Speak their fond fare- well. Ni - ta! Jua - ni - ta! Ask thy soul if
To a pray'r gone by? Ni - ta! Jua - ni - ta! Let me lin - ger

we should part! Ni - ta! Jua - ni - ta! Lean thou on my heart.
by thy side! Ni - ta! Jua - ni - ta! Be my own fair bride.

My Bonnie

Nut Brown Maiden

Moderato

1. Nut brown maid - en, Thou hast a bright blue eye for love,
2. Nut brown maid - en, Thou hast a ru - by lip to kiss,
3. Nut brown maid - en, Thou hast a slen - der waist to clasp,

Nut brown maid - en, Thou hast a bright blue eye, A
Nut brown maid - en, Thou hast a ru - by lip, A
Nut brown maid - en, Thou hast a slen - der waist, A

bright blue eye is thine, love! The glance in it is mine, love!
ru - by lip is thine, love! The kiss - ing of it's mine, love!
slen - der waist is thine, love! The arm a - round it's mine, love!

Nut brown maid - en, Thou hast a bright blue eye for love,
Nut brown maid - en, Thou hast a ru - by lip to kiss,
Nut brown maid - en, Thou hast a slen - der waist to clasp,

Nut brown maid - en, Thou hast a bright blue eye.
Nut brown maid - en, Thou hast a bright blue eye.
Nut brown maid - en, Thou hast a bright blue eye.

The Spanish Cavalier

WM. D. HENDRICKSON